They Shall Not Pass

by

Andy Croft

Illustrated by Alan Marks

In memory of Tommy Chilvers, Dave
Goodman, John Longstaff
and Dave Marshall

With special thanks to:

Tom Shaw
Fred Smith
Oliver Smith
Sebastian Vetterlein

First published in 2009 in Great Britain by
Barrington Stoke Ltd
18 Walker St, Edinburgh, EH3 7LP

www.barringtonstoke.co.uk

Copyright © 2009 Andy Croft
Illustrations © Alan Marks

The moral right of the author has been asserted in
accordance with the Copyright, Designs and
Patents Act 1988

ISBN: 978-1-84299-707-9

Printed in Great Britain by Bell & Bain Ltd

Contents

A Note from the Author

This story is based on real events that took place over 70 years ago. On 4 October 1936, Oswald Mosley and his Black Shirts tried to march through the East End of London. Like the Nazis in Germany, they were against anyone who was a Jew. Like the BNP today, they wanted to stir up anger and hate against people of a different race.

250,000 Londoners came out onto the streets to stop them. Some of them were Jews, but most of them were not. They were against the Black Shirts. They were on the side of freedom for all people, of all races. They were crowded onto the pavements.

There was no space left. They blocked the streets. They wouldn't let the Black Shirts past.

The police tried to force a way down Cable Street for the Black Shirts. The police were on their side. Some people were hurt. Lots of people were arrested. But still Oswald Mosley and the Black Shirts couldn't get past. It became known as "The Battle of Cable Street".

Today hatred of people of different races is back again. In fact, the "racists" are stronger than ever.

Which side are you on?

Chapter 1
East Enders

70 years ago every street had its own

gang. The Nelson Street gang was just Nat,

Joe, Harry and me, Sam. Nelson Street was

named after the famous English hero,

Admiral Nelson.

I was always a bit of a fighter and handy

with my fists. I had to be. The East End of

London was a hard place. You had to stand up for yourself.

I wanted to be a hero. Like Nelson. I wanted to be big and strong, like Tarzan. Like the boxers Billy Wells and Kid Berg. They were both British champions. And they were both from Stepney, my part of London. In fact, they were both born on Cable Street. Just round the corner from Nelson Street.

4

The gang used to meet after school outside the sweet shop on the corner. We played marbles. We collected old tram-tickets and swapped cigarette-cards. We collected old rags and jam-jars and sold them to the rag and bone man who came past most weeks with his horse and cart. In the winter we went to Victoria Park to watch the football. In summer we played at Cowboys and Indians.

5

Sometimes we had fights with other gangs. Nothing bad. Mostly a lot of name-calling and stone-throwing. The worst fights were against kids from the other side of the main road. They were mostly Irish. We called them the "Yoks". And they called us the "Yids".

6

We were Jewish, you see. Most of the families on our side of the road were Jewish refugees. Our grandparents had come to Britain from Poland and Russia. They came to make a better life for their families. To escape being poor. Or to escape being murdered in their beds. In those days people hated Jews in places like Poland and Russia. They used to blame the Jews for everything.

7

In London we were still poor. But at least we felt safe. As long as we didn't cross the main road.

One night we were playing football under the lamp-post at the end of our street. Jumpers for goalposts. Joe was trying out his goal-kicks. He kicked the ball so hard it went down New Road. We all ran after it.

The Cannon Street kids were waiting for us on the other side of the road. They started pelting us with stones, shouting "Yids! Yids!" The leader was a tall boy with curly red hair. He was a good shot. A stone flew past my ear. Another one hit me on the hand. I felt he was aiming at me. I wanted to punch him. But I couldn't get near him. We moved back, out of range of their stones. The Cannon Street kids started cheering. The boy with red hair made a jungle-call like Tarzan.

"Come on, Sam," said Nat. "Let's go home."

"We'll be back," I yelled, dodging a flying milk-bottle. "Just you wait!"

"Oh, yeah?" the boy with red hair grinned. "You and whose army?"

Chapter 2
Alf

When I was fourteen I left school. I got a job working for a carpenter. It was hard work. I had to carry planks of wood around in a barrow all day. Eight in the morning until seven at night. Saturday mornings as well. All for just a few shillings a week. But it was a job.

11

I had only been there a few weeks when the boss called me to his office.

"Sam," he said to me, "this is Alf, the new boy. He'll be working with you."

It was the boy with red hair from Cannon Street.

Neither of us said anything for a moment. Then the boy held out his hand. "Me Tarzan," he grinned. I grinned back and shook his hand.

By the end of that day Alf and I were friends. By the end of the week we were best friends. I showed him how to load the barrows, and how to turn corners. He showed me how to make a jungle-call like Tarzan. We swapped cigarette-cards. I lent him some of my comics. He let me try out his catapult.

Alf's mother was from Wales. His father was Irish and worked in the docks. But most of the time he didn't have a job. Alf was scared of his dad. Once he came to work with a black eye. I asked him how he got it. But he didn't want to talk about it.

14

Alf and I did everything together. It
didn't matter that we came from different
streets. We were best mates. He took me to
meet the Cannon Street gang. We swapped
marbles. Alf's best cat's-eye marble for one
of my steelies. I took him back with me to
meet Nat, Joe and Harry.

We once all went to see a Tarzan film. It
was great. After it was over we ran home,

15

thumping our chests like Tarzan. We pretended that we were kings of the jungle. The East End in those days was a bit of a jungle. There were some very nasty people about. You had to watch out for the crocodiles.

Chapter 3
Rose

One Saturday Alf and I were standing outside the café on Mile End Road. We often went there on a Saturday night. There were always lots of kids, all talking and laughing and showing off. We were just about to go home when Alf dug me in the ribs.

"Hey – look at those two," he said.

Two girls about our age were walking towards us, arm in arm. One girl was dark and tall. The other had long fair hair. They were looking at us and giggling.

Alf stepped out in front of them and thumped his chest.

"Me Tarzan," he said to the girl with the dark hair. "You Jane." And he did his jungle-call. The girls smiled.

"I'm not called Jane," grinned the girl with the dark hair. "My name is Jess. And this is Rose."

Rose blushed. Like a flower, I thought. An English rose.

We began to talk. Or rather, Alf and Jess did all the talking. I couldn't take my eyes off Rose. She was the prettiest girl I had ever seen. She and Jess worked in a clothes factory. Jess lived near us. Rose lived on Cable Street, on the other side of the main road. Her father worked on the docks. We told them we were skilled carpenters. I don't think they believed us.

After that, the four of us met every Saturday night outside the café. Sometimes we went inside for fish and chips. Sometimes we walked round the Saturday night market, looking at all the things we couldn't buy. One night we all went to see a film. Alf sat next to Jess. I sat next to Rose. I don't remember much about the film. But Rose and I held hands in the dark.

The next Saturday Alf didn't turn up. Jess tried to pretend she didn't mind. The three of us walked about for a bit. But it wasn't the same without Alf.

He turned up at work on Monday with a new black eye. I asked him how he got it.

21

But he just shrugged and said something about helping his dad. He seemed cold and distant. He wouldn't look at me. Like he had something on his mind.

I soon found out what it was.

Chapter 4
Because

At first I thought that Alf was joking. I couldn't believe it. We were eating our sandwiches at work. By now Alf's black eye was starting to turn yellow.

"I just think you should stay away from Rose. She's too good for you."

I didn't understand. Of course Rose was too good for me. I didn't need Alf to tell me that.

"What do you mean?" I asked.

"You know."

"Know what?"

Alf frowned. "Look, Sam. Don't make me say it."

"Say what?" I was really puzzled. "Stop talking in riddles, Alf. Why should I stay away from Rose?"

"Because I say so."

"Because you say so?" I was starting to lose my temper.

Alf took a deep breath. "Because Rose is English. She should be going out with someone better than you."

I stared at him. "What does that mean?"

Then I saw it all. Alf wanted to go out with Rose. That's why he had stopped seeing Jess. That's why he wanted me to give up Rose.

"You don't belong here," Alf said. "You're not English."

"What?" I was really puzzled now. "I'm as English as you are," I replied.

"My dad says you should go back to Russia!"

"But I'm not from Russia – I'm from Nelson Street! I was born in London. Here in Stepney. Same as you. Anyway, your family's from Ireland!"

"That's different. We're Christians. Jews and Christians have always been enemies."

"I thought Christians were told to love their enemies?"

"Don't try and be clever with me," snapped Alf. "My dad says there are big changes coming. The Black Shirts are going to get rid of the Jews. And then we'll all be rich."

"But –"

"He says I can't be friends with you. Or Jess. He says you're dirty Yids!"

"And I say he's stupid! And so are you if you listen to him."

Alf was angry now. But not as angry as I was.

"It's time you stood up to your dad. He's just a bully – look at your right eye!"

For a second I thought Alf was going to cry. Then he swung his fist at my head.

"You leave my dad out of this!" he yelled. I ducked and whacked him on the chest.

"And you keep your hands off Rose!" I yelled.

"Too late," Alf grinned. "She's mine now."

"Who says?"

"She does. She told me so last night. She said you were a smelly Yid!"

I really went for him then. I smacked him on the nose. He tried to punch me. But I ducked and hit him again. He grabbed me round the neck. We fell back, snapping a chair and knocking over a new desk. The desk smashed to the floor with a great crash.

By the time the boss pulled us apart we were a right mess. So was the workshop. The boss told us both to clear off. And not come back.

Chapter 5
It's a Free Country

I'd heard about the Black Shirts. They wanted to be like the Nazis in Germany. Their leader was a toff called Oswald Mosley. He wanted to be the English Hitler.

I'd seen the Black Shirts on the news at the cinema. I thought they looked stupid. They blamed the Jews for everything. They

33

said we had too much money. They said we had too little money. They said we worked too hard. They said we were lazy. They said we didn't belong in Britain.

Now they were starting to march around parts of the East End. You could see them striding up and down in their black shirts yelling, "Yids! Yids! We gotta get rid of the Yids!" One night an old Jew was beaten up in the next street. The windows of some Jewish shops were broken. Someone chalked "Kill the Dirty Yids" on the walls. Things were getting bad.

Then the Black Shirts said they were

going to march through Stepney. Everyone

was talking about it. Everyone was excited.

That Sunday morning the streets were

buzzing. My brother said someone should

stand up to them.

"Just make sure it isn't you," said my mother. "I don't want you getting into trouble. We've got enough heroes in this family already." She glared at me. My face was still a mess.

My brother was reading the *Daily Worker*. "It says here that 100,000 people have signed up against the Black Shirts.

They want the police to stop the march. But they won't."

"I'm sure the police know what they're doing," said my mother.

"But they can't just march through our streets," said my brother.

"It's a free country," said my mother.

"Yes, but it won't be if the Black Shirts get their way."

"Well, it's nothing to do with us." She shrugged.

"That's what you think!" My brother slammed out of the house.

I got up to follow him.

"Where do you think you're going?" my mother asked.

"Just out," I said.

She gave a sigh. "Don't you go getting involved, Sam, will you?"

"Of course not," I said.

"Promise?"

"I promise!"

She did not have to worry. I wasn't interested in politics. I had enough to think about. I had to find another job. And I had to see Rose. Even if it meant going onto enemy ground.

Chapter 6
The Battle of Cable Street

The fastest way to Cable Street was past Alf's house. I made up my mind to take the long way round. I hadn't seen Rose for two weeks. Not since the fight. For one thing, my face was still black and blue and covered in cuts. For another I had no money. And I was scared of Alf and his gang. But what if she was going out with Alf? I had to see her.

There were a lot of people about for a Sunday morning. The road was thick with crowds of people. Old and young, men and women, Jews and non-Jews. Old soldiers stood on the pavements. They were proudly wearing their medals. Loud-speaker vans were dashing up and down, telling everyone to come out and stop the Black Shirts and their march. There were first-aid posts in the doorways of shops. It was like a battle-field.

It took me almost an hour to reach the corner. I had never seen so many people.

There were thousands of policemen in
uniform. They were trying to force the
crowd back. I had no chance of getting to
Rose's house that way. I pushed my way
down a back alley.

When I reached Cable Street it was packed with people. The noise was awful. Everyone was shouting, "They Shall Not Pass! They Shall Not Pass!" A police plane was flying over the crowd. I climbed a lamp-post to see what was going on.

The Black Shirts were trying to march down Cable Street. Some dockers had pushed a lorry over in the middle of the street. The police were trying to move it. They were hitting the crowd with batons. Some of the police were shouting, "Dirty Jews!" People were getting hurt. But Cable Street was very narrow. The crowd couldn't move back. I saw some people being pushed through shop windows. Some old women were throwing milk-bottles at the police from a bedroom window. There was broken glass everywhere. It was like a war.

The police moved the lorry. But some women were throwing bits of chairs and beds onto the road. People were building more road-blocks across the street.

Then I saw her. Rose was trying to lift a table onto the pile. It was too big for her. I pushed through the crowd and ran over to help.

45

"Sam!" she gasped. "What have you done to your face?"

"Never mind. Where's Alf?"

"Alf?" Rose frowned. "Don't talk about him. He's over there with those stupid Black Shirts. He told me you didn't want to see me any more. Because I'm not Jewish."

"But –" I begain to say, "Alf said –"

At that moment the police charged towards us on their horses. The horses were huge.

Their hooves were clattering on the road. There was no time to run. The policemen had their batons out. They were almost on top of us. Rose yelled. I grabbed her hand and held it tight.

Suddenly the horses were slipping and falling over. A policeman fell off his horse. A cheer went up behind us. Someone was throwing marbles under the horses' hooves! I turned round. It was Nat, Joe, Harry and the Cannon Street gang. Another horse slipped over. The police started to pull back. Another cheer went up. "They Shall Not Pass!" shouted the crowd, "They Shall Not Pass!"

And they didn't. Soon after this the police gave up. Without the police the Black Shirts stood no chance. When they saw that they couldn't get down Cable Street they turned round and marched off home. The

Black Shirts had lost. London had won the battle for freedom.

That night there was a party in Victoria Park. Everyone was there. All the kids from Nelson Street and Cannon Street came. Only Alf was missing. He had chosen to join the Black Shirts.

Of course I was sorry about that. His father was a bully. It's hard to stand up to bullies. It is sometimes easier to join them. And that's what Alf did.

As we walked home Rose and I held hands again. No one and nothing was going to come between us now.

Chapter 7
The Fight Goes On

After that day me and the gang went on fighting for freedom. We fought against Hitler's friends in Spain. In the Second World War we fought against Hitler's armies in North Africa and Italy. That's when I lost my leg.

51

When I came home I went back to being a carpenter. Not pushing a wheel-barrow this time. Making nice furniture. Good stuff. I'm writing this on a desk I made.

I gave up work several years ago. Rose and I have seven grandchildren. And four great-grandchildren. We still live in Stepney. Not far from Cable Street.

I saw Alf in the local paper a while back. He and his sons run a chain of shops in the East End. He supports the BNP these days. Still trying to stir up anger and hatred. This time it's against the Muslims, people from India and Pakistan. People from the

West Indies. People from Africa and Asia. They seem to hate anyone who is different.

Well, I'm different. So are you. Everyone is different. We all like different food and different music. We wear different clothes and sing different songs. But we are all the same under the skin. People come to Britain from all over the world. Most are escaping from war and hunger. I am proud that we make them welcome.

Britain's a great country. And it's worth fighting for. Not with your fists. I learned that a long time ago. There are other ways to fight. It's no good fighting on your own.

You need to know what you are fighting for.

And you need to know who your friends are.

Under Cover of Darkness

by
Pat Thomson

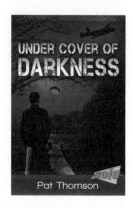

The Nazis have arrived in Michel's village. But the Resistance are fighting back. Can Michel help to win the secret war?

You can order *Under Cover of Darkness* from our website at www.barringtonstoke.co.uk

The Dunkirk Escape

by
Jim Eldridge

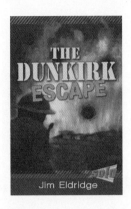

Dave Jones is trapped on the beach at Dunkirk, as bombs explode all around him. Can his son Tom get there in time to save him?

You can order *The Dunkirk Escape* from our website at www.barringtonstoke.co.uk

Flash Flood

by
Andy Croft

Jaz and Toni are trapped and the water is rising ... Can they make it out in time?

You can order *Flash Flood* from our website at
www.barringtonstoke.co.uk

Cliff Edge
by
Jane A. C. West

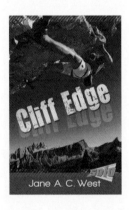

Can Danny make the climb of his life to save his friend?
No ropes, no help – no hope?

You can order *Cliff Edge* from our website at
www.barringtonstoke.co.uk